NEW PIANO SERIES

INTRODUCTORY ALBUM

FREDERICK
HARRIS
MUSIC

Official Examination Repertoire and Studies of The Royal Conservatory of Music - Introductory Grade
Répertoire et études officiels des examens du Royal Conservatory of Music - Niveau introductoire

NEW PIANO SERIES

The *New Piano Series* is designed to serve the needs of teachers and students, as well as those who play the piano solely for their own enjoyment. Once a student has completed an entry level method or course, he or she will be ready for the Introductory Album of the *New Piano Series*. This Album is a musical resource for beginning pianists of all ages. Imaginative and enjoyable pieces have been chosen in order to expand the musical horizons of students. The Introductory Album leads naturally to the Repertoire Album 1 and the Studies Album 1 & 2 of the *New Piano Series*. A recording of the Introductory Album is available to assist in the study and enjoyment of the music.

A Note on Editing

Most Baroque composers wrote few dynamics, articulation, or other performance indications in their scores. Interpretation was left up to the performer, with the expectation that the performance practice was understood. In this edition, therefore, most of the dynamics and tempo indications in the Baroque pieces have been added by the editors. These editorial markings, including fingering, are intended to be helpful rather than definitive.

By the late 18th century, composers for the piano included more performance indications in their scores, a trend which became standard in the 19th century. Therefore, in late Classical and Romantic compositions, as well as in the music of our own time, the performer is able to rely on the composers' own markings to a greater extent.

A Note on Performance Practice

The keyboard instruments of the 17th and early to mid-18th centuries lacked the sustaining power of the modern piano. Consequently, the usual keyboard touch was detached rather than legato. The pianist should assume that a lightly articulated touch is appropriate for the Baroque and early Classical music, unless a different approach is indicated either in the music or in a footnote. Slurs are used to indicate legato notes or short phrases.

Piano Syllabus - RCM Examinations

The Royal Conservatory of Music Piano Syllabus gives full details regarding examinations. Teachers, students, and parents are urged to consult the most recent Syllabus for current examination requirements and procedures.

Note au sujet de l'édition

La plupart des compositeurs baroques et classiques ne notaient ni nuances ni articulations dans leurs partitions. L'interprète était libre de jouer comme il l'entendait en basant bien sûr son interprétation sur la norme de son époque. Dans cette édition la majeure partie des nuances et articulations trouvées dans les pièces baroques et classiques ont été ajoutées par les éditeurs. Ces additions, incluant doigtés et ornementation, sont fournies à titre indicatif seulement.

A partir de la fin du 18ème siècle les compositeurs commencèrent à inclure de plus en plus d'indications dans leurs partitions. L'interprète de musique de la fin du classique jusqu'à nos jours peut donc beaucoup plus faire appel aux indications du compositeur.

Note au sujet de l'exécution

Les claviers du 17ème et début du 18ème siècles n'avaient pas le ton soutenu d'un piano moderne. Conséquemment l'articulation était surtout détaché plutôt que legato. Le pianiste devrait donc approcher la musique baroque et début du classique avec une légère articulation à moins qu'une approche différente ne soit indiquée dans la partition ou par une note de l'éditeur. Le legato et de courtes phrases sont indiqués par des liaisons.

Piano Syllabus - Examens du RCM

Le Piano Syllabus du Royal Conservatory of Music contient tous les détails au sujet des examens. Il est impératif pour les professeurs, élèves et parents de consulter le plus récent Syllabus pour être au courant des pré-requis et des règles des examens.

Introductory Album
TABLE OF CONTENTS

* Canadian composer / Compositeur canadien

A 16TH-CENTURY MARCH / MARCHE DU SEIZIÈME SIÈCLE

LIST A

Anonymous /
Anonyme

Source: *Creating Music*, Recital Book Two

© Copyright 1973 Alfred Publishing Co. Inc. Used by permission of the publisher.

OLD RUSSIAN SONG / VIEILLE CHANSON RUSSE

LIST A

Pyotr Il'yich Tchaikovsky
(1840 - 1893)

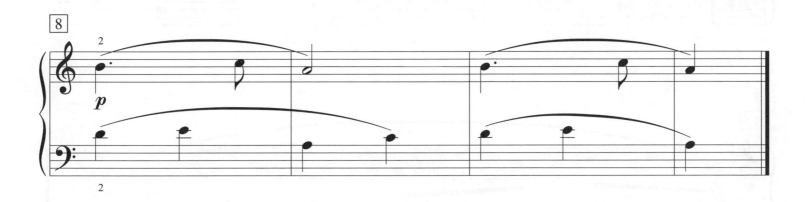

YOUTHFUL JOY / JOIE JUVÉNILE

LIST A

Daniel Gottlob Türk
(1750 - 1813)

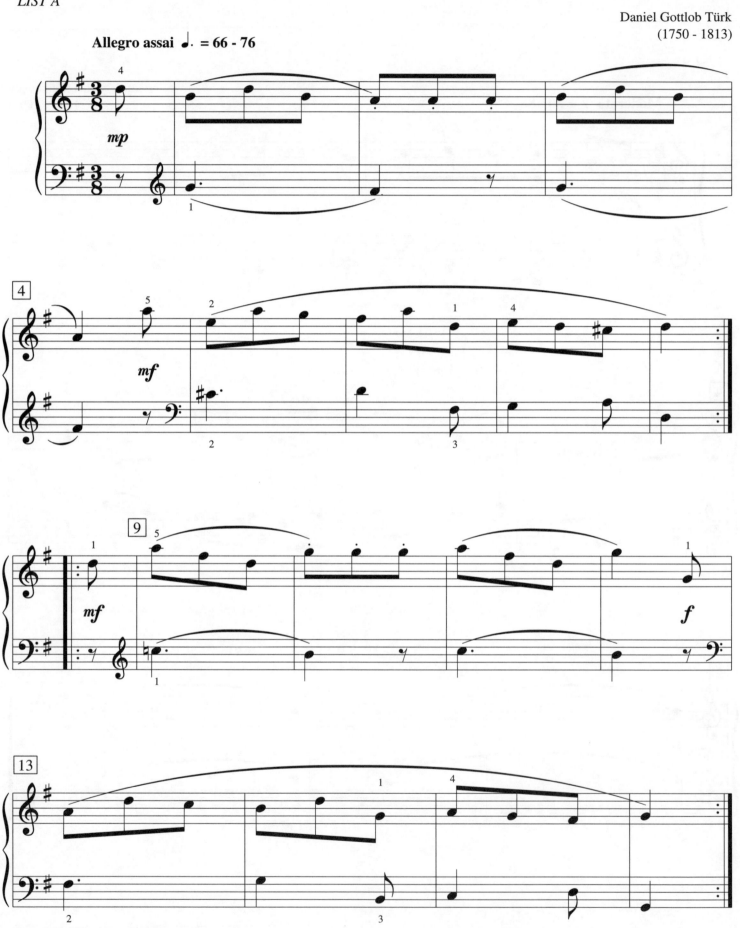

Original title / Titre originale: "Jugendlich froh"
Source: *Handstücke für angehende Klavierspieler* [Pieces for Aspiring Keyboard Players / Pièces pour pianistes débutants], vol. 1 (1792)

A SAD SONG / CHANSON TRISTE

LIST A

P. Lvov-Kompaniets

RUSSIAN SONG / CHANSON RUSSE

LIST A

T. Saliutrinskaya

Source: *Fortepiano, First Year / Fortepiano, l'année première*

A CUCKOO IN THE WOODS / UN COUCOU DANS LES BOIS

LIST A

Allegretto ♩ = 120 - 132

A. Kranz

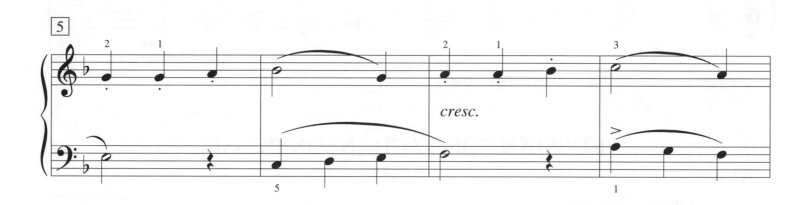

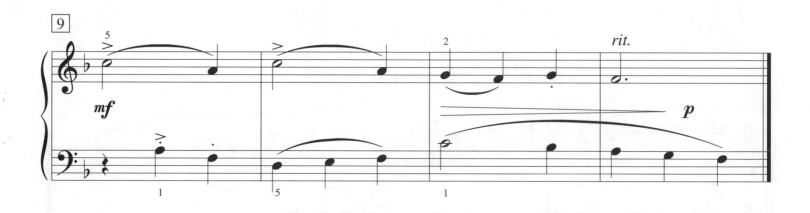

Source: *Fortepiano, First Year / Fortepiano, l'année première*
© Copyright 1974 Muzyka Ukraine. Used by permission.

PLAYING SOLDIERS / EN JOUANT AUX SOLDATS

LIST A

Renée Christopher
(1955 -   )

March time / à la marcia

CRADLE SONG / BERCEUSE

LIST A

Daniel Gottlob Türk
(1750 - 1813)

Andantino

THE NEW DOLLY DANCES /
LA NOUVELLE POUPÉE DANSE

(for / pour Alexa)

LIST B

Jean Coulthard
(1908 -   )

Happily - not too fast /
Gaiement - pas trop vite ♩ = 108 - 120

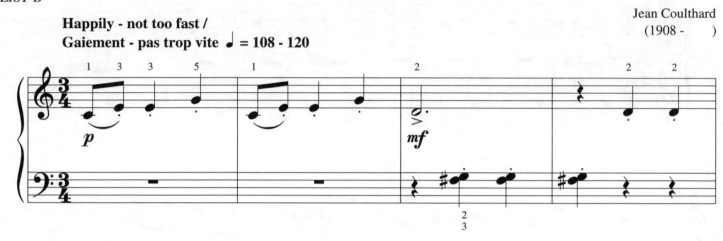

Slower - Dolly lost her shoe! /
Plus lent - La poupée a perdu son soulier!

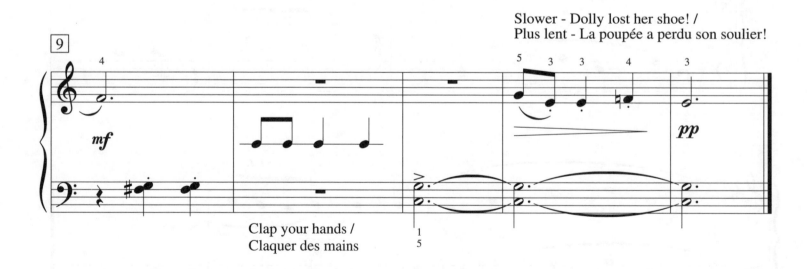

Clap your hands /
Claquer des mains

TEASING / TAQUINERIES

LIST B

Pierre Gallant
(1950 -   )

Playfully / Enjoué ♩ = 76 - 84

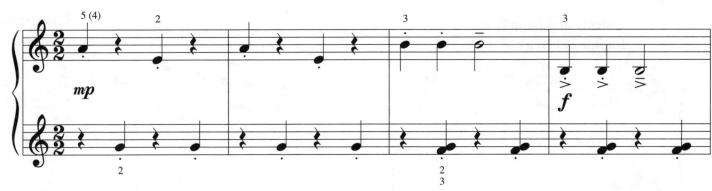

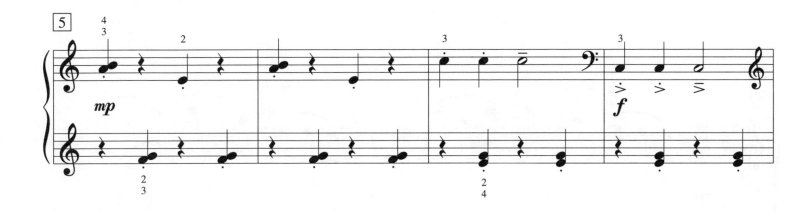

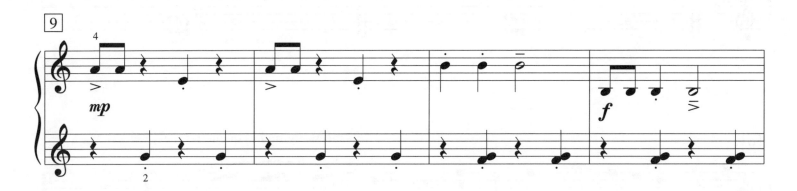

PLAYFUL PUPPY / CHIOT ESPIÈGLE

LIST B

Linda Niamath
(1939 -   )

Quickly and happily /
Rapide et joyeux ♩ = 96 - 104

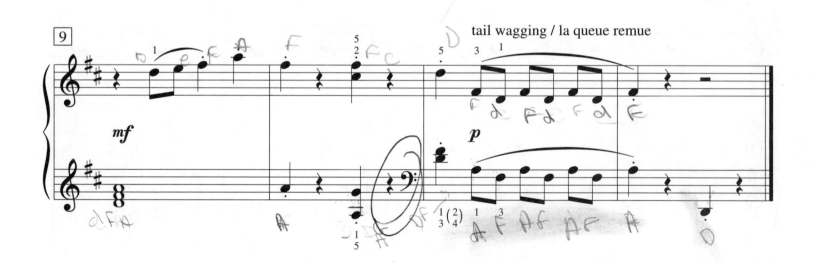

tail wagging / la queue remue

Source: *Soda Pop and Other Delights*
© Copyright 1982 The Frederick Harris Music Co., Limited.

THE MARCHING PIGS / LA MARCHE DES COCHONS

LIST B

Boris Berlin
(1907 -   )

In march time / Tempo de marche ♩ = 88 - 100

Source: *Our Animal Friends*

© Copyright 1940 by Gordon V. Thompson Music, A Division of Warner / Chappell Music Canada Ltd., Toronto, Ontario.
Reprinted by permission.

CRADLE SONG / BERCEUSE

LIST B

Brian Crone
(1957 -   )

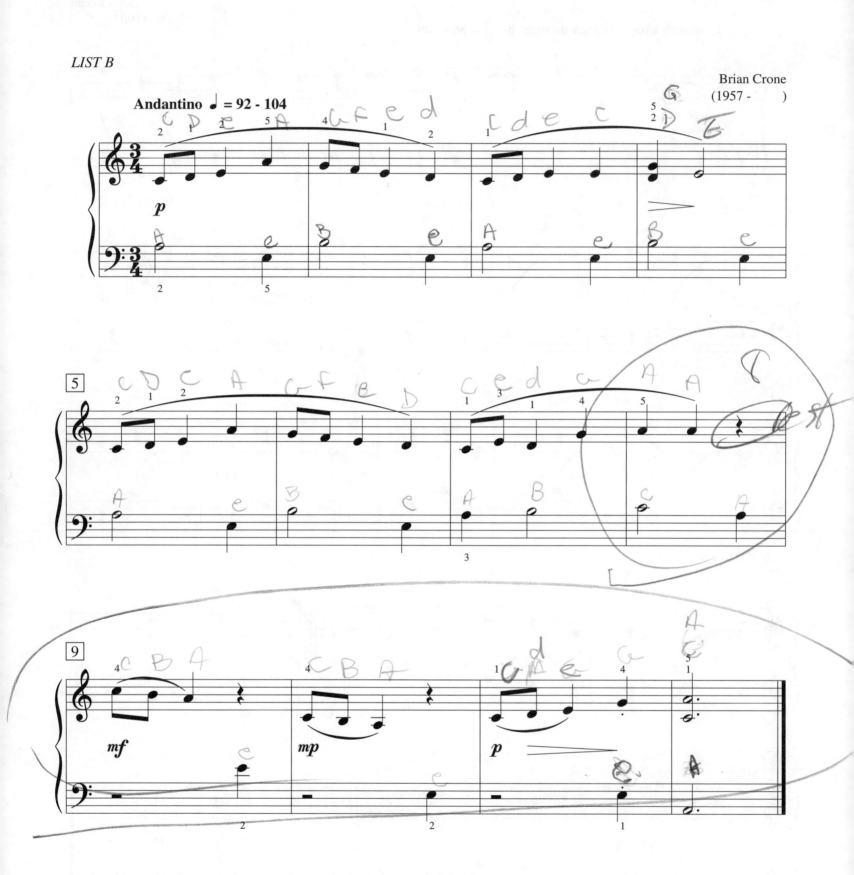

BROKEN MUSIC BOX / LA BOÎTE À MUSIQUE EST CASSÉE

LIST B

Stephen Chatman
(1950 -   )

**Moderately; sweetly /
modéré; doux**

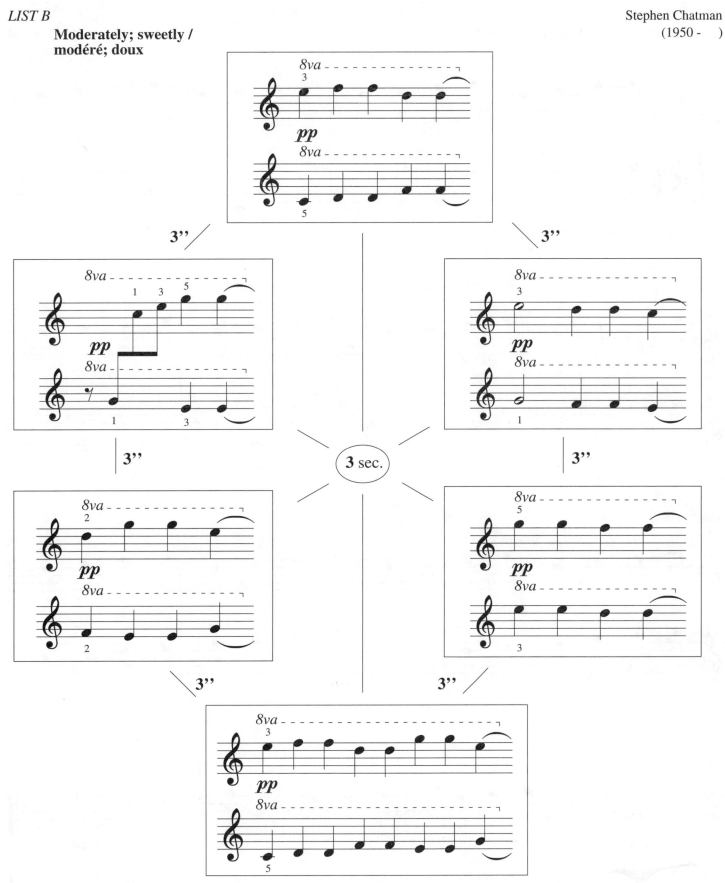

1. Hold pedal from beginning to end. / Abaisser la pédale du début à la fin.

2. Begin by playing any box. Proceed with any progression of boxes until you decide to end the piece. / Commencer en jouant n'importe quelle boîte, continuer avec n'importe quelle succession de boîtes jusqu'à ce que vous décidiez de terminer la pièce.

3. 3'' = approximate number of seconds between the end of one box and the beginning of the next. / 3" = nombre approximatif de secondes entre la fin d'une boîte et le début de la suivante.

Source: *Amusements,* Book 2

CHIMES / CARILLONS

LIST B

Broadly / Large ♩ = 88 - 104

Paul Sheftel

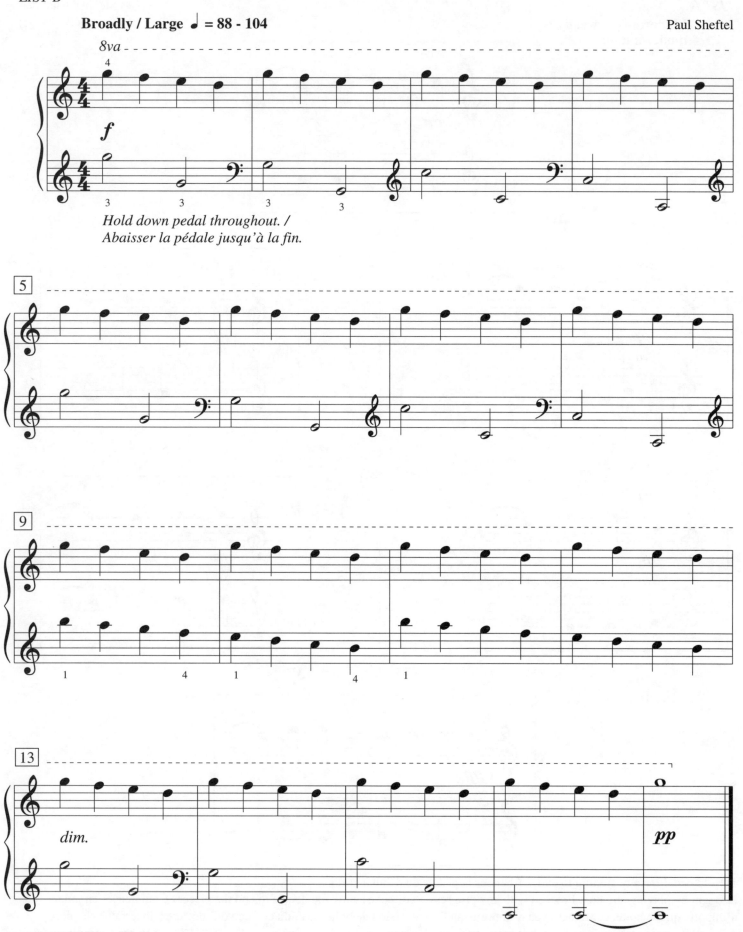

Hold down pedal throughout. /
Abaisser la pédale jusqu'à la fin.

Source: *Merry and Mellow*

HALLOWE'EN PRANKS / FÊTONS L'HALLOWE'EN

LIST B

Boris Berlin
(1907 -   )

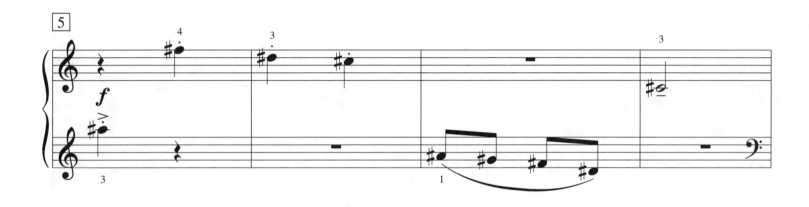

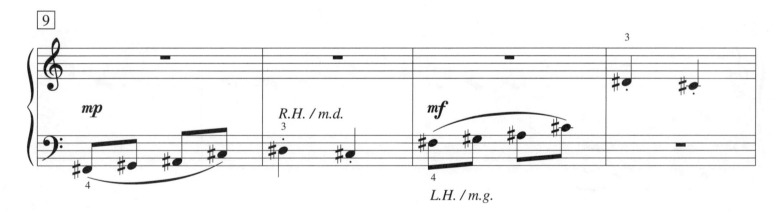

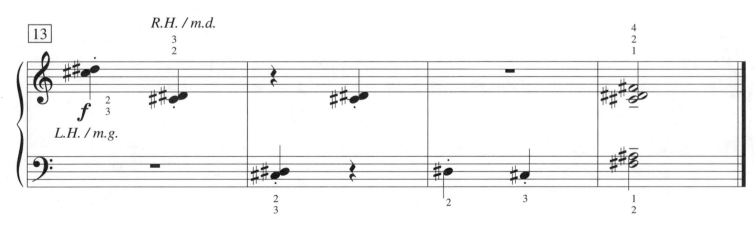

Source: *The ABC of Piano Playing*, Book 3
© Copyright 1985 The Frederick Harris Music Co., Limited.

THE FAMOUS HAUNTED HOUSE /
LA CÉLÈBRE MAISON HANTÉE

LIST B

Spooky / Fantomatique ♩ = 126 - 132

Lynn Freeman Olson
(1938 - 1987)

Source: *Music Pathways*

ON THE MOVE / EN MARCHE

LIST B

Lynn Freeman Olson
(1938 - 1987)

Brightly / Avec éclat ♩. = 96 - 112

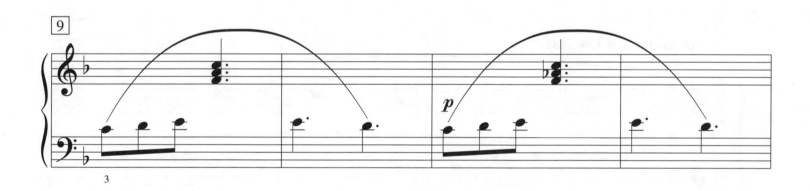

Source: Music Pathways

JUMPING JACKS / LES PANTINS

LIST C

Andrew Markow
(1942 -   )

LYDIAN MELODY / MÉLODIE LYDIENNE

LIST C

Lajos Papp
(1935 -   )

Source: *Starting the Piano / En commençant le piano*

ABC

LIST C

Martin Frey
(1872 - 1946)

In a happy mood /
Enjoué ♩ = 84 - 96

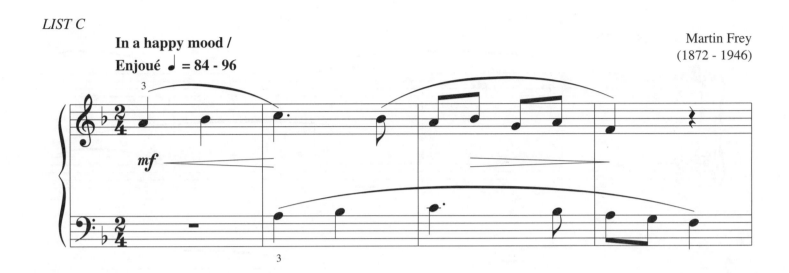

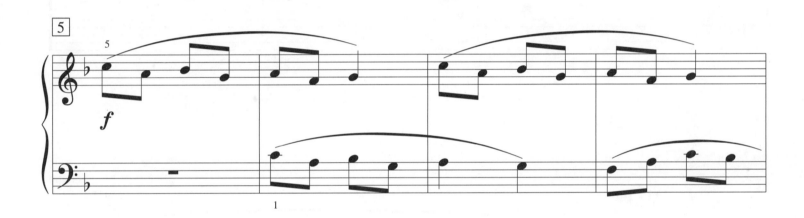

TWO RESPONSES / DEUX RÉPONSES

I

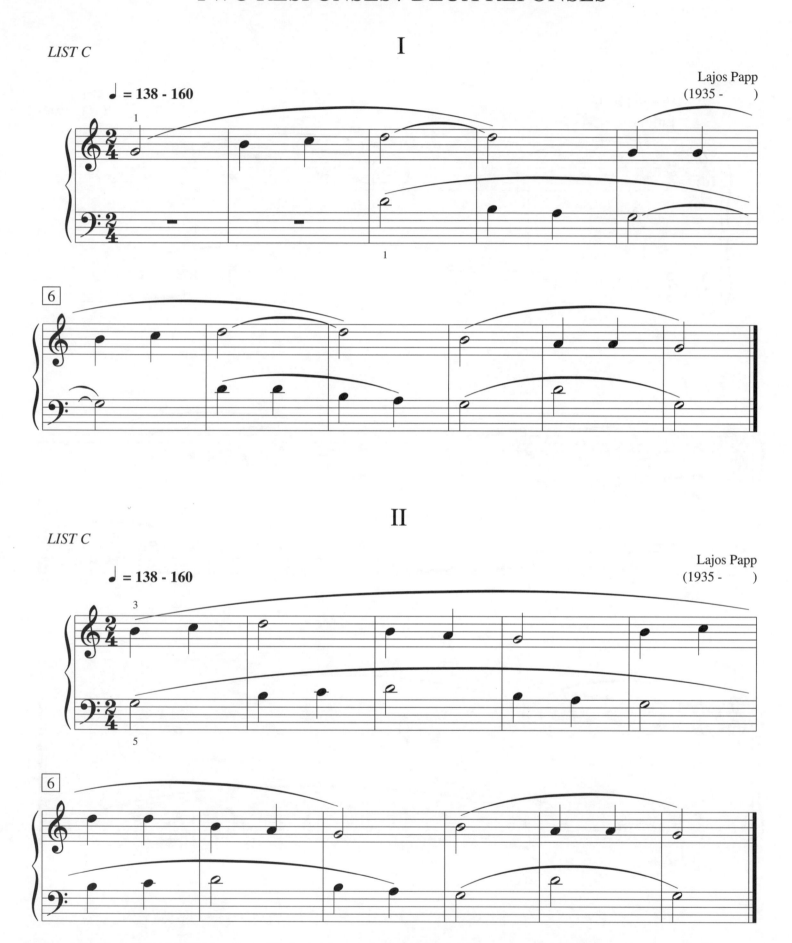

N. B.: Both pieces are to be played as one selection at examinations. / Les deux pièces doivent être jouées comme un ensemble aux examens.

Source: *Starting the Piano / En commençant le piano*

© Copyright 1973 Editio Musica Budapest. Used by permission.

DIALOGUE

LIST C

Béla Bartók
(1881 - 1945)

Moderato ♩ = 116 - 132

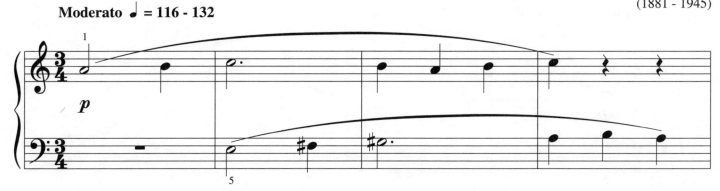

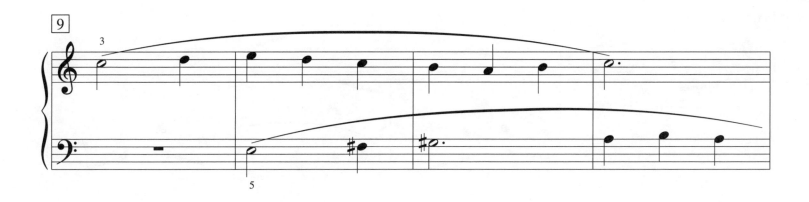

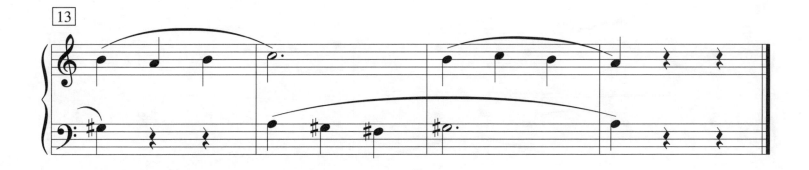

Source: *The First Term at the Piano / Initiation au piano* (1913)

QUESTIONING / INTERROGATION

LIST C

Pierre Gallant
(1950 -   )

STUDY NO. 1 / ÉTUDE N° 1
March and Run / Marche et course

Joan Last
(1908 -   )

Source: *Gymnastics*
© Copyright 1979 Boosey and Hawkes Music Publishers Ltd. Used with publisher's permission.

STUDY NO. 2 / ÉTUDE N° 2
Jack and Jill / Jack et Jill

Renée Christopher
(1955 -   )

m.d. = *mano destra* (R.H. / m.d.); *m.s.* = *mano sinistra* (L.H. / m.g.)
© Copyright 1994 The Frederick Harris Music Co., Limited.

STUDY NO. 3 / ÉTUDE Nº 3

Trampoline

Joan Last
(1908 -   )

With a bouncy rhythm / Rythme sautillant ♩. = 69 - 80

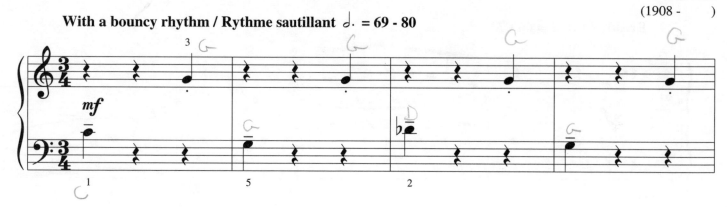

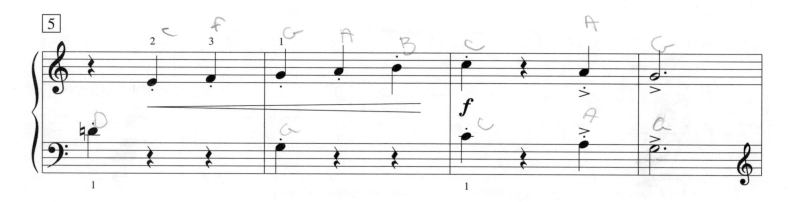

Source: *Gymnastics*

STUDY NO. 4 / ÉTUDE N° 4
Soaring High / Envol vers les hauteurs

Stephen Chatman
(1950 -   )

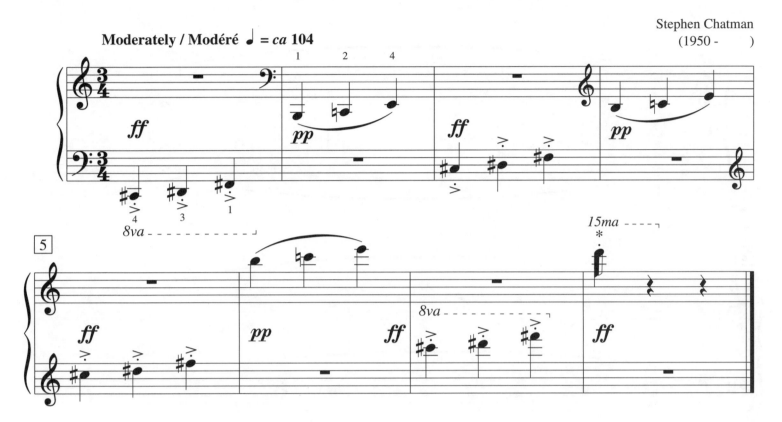

Nose Dive / Descente en piqué

Stephen Chatman
(1950 -   )

* = Black and white note cluster within given pitch range / Cluster de touches blanches et noires dans l'intervalle donné

N. B.: Both pieces are to be played as one selection at examinations. / Les deux pièces doivent être jouées comme un ensemble aux examens.

Source: *Amusements*, Book 1

© Copyright 1989 The Frederick Harris Music Co., Limited.

STUDY NO. 5 / ÉTUDE N° 5
Contrary Motion / Mouvement contraire

Béla Bartók
(1881 - 1945)

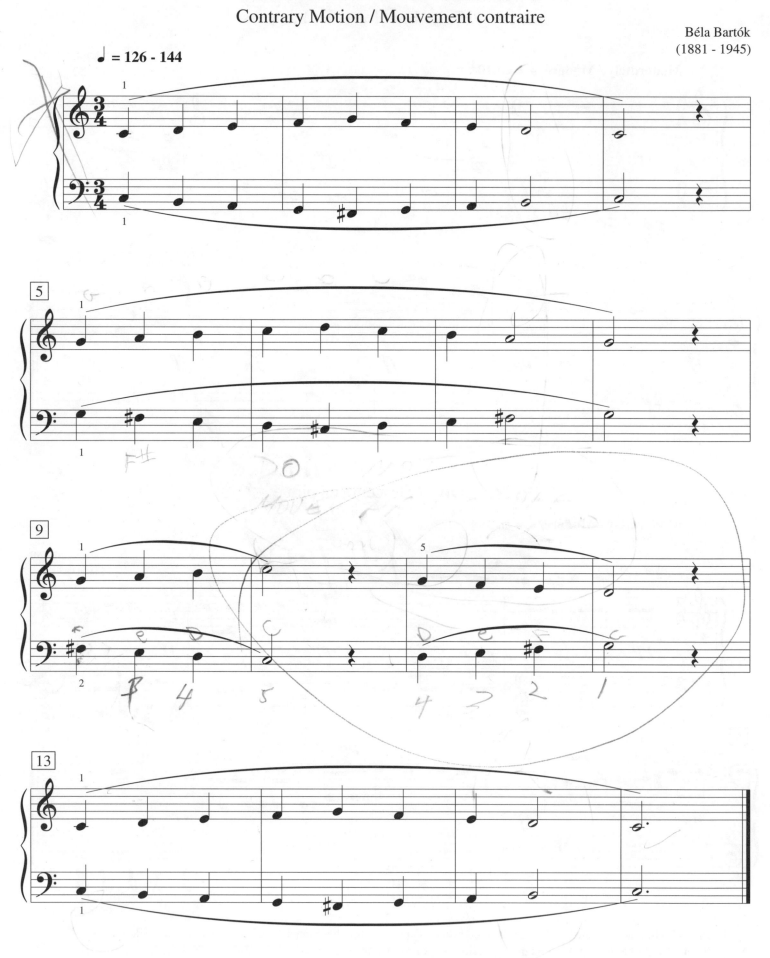

Source: *Mikrokosmos*, Vol. 1, No. 17